How Many Legs, How Many Toes?

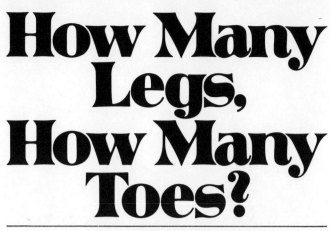

A Beginning Book About Animals

By MARY ELTING

Pictures by CYNTHIA and ALVIN KOEHLER

WONDER BOOKS · NEW YORK

A Division of Grosset & Dunlap, Inc.

A National General Company

INTRODUCTION

Why do boys and girls ask questions? Mostly because they want answers. But sometimes they also want to wonder out loud. A question can tell as well as ask. It can tell about the surprising things that grownups take for granted.

And so this book was designed for children and grownups to explore together. We have called it a Beginning Book because it is an invitation to wonder and to begin finding out. In words and pictures it offers the youngest questioners a chance to think—and to discover some answers for themselves.

Library of Congress Catalog Card Number: 71-175630

ISBN: 0-448-04500-1 (Wonder Trade Edition)
ISBN: 0-448-03617-7 (Library Edition)

You have pockets in your clothes.

What has a pocket but NO clothes?

A mother kangaroo has a pocket.

Away she goes with her baby in her pocket.

A mother opossum has a pocket.
Her babies go to bed in her pocket.

Then they wake up!
How many are there?

A father sea horse has a special pocket.
He can carry a hundred sea horse eggs in it.
They hatch.
Out come the baby sea horses.

This baby sea horse has a ride.

You have ten fingers.
You can pinch.

What can pinch without any fingers?

A lobster hasn't any fingers,
but it can pinch.
It catches food with its claws.

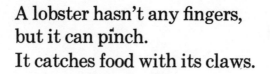

So does a crab.

You have two arms and two legs.
So do monkeys.

What has eight arms and no legs?

An octopus.
It catches food with its arms.

What has NO arms and eight legs?

A spider.

There are spiders of many kinds.

These birds have wings for flying.

What has wings but can't fly?

An ostrich has wings, and it can't
fly.
But it can run very fast.

A penguin has wings. It can't
fly, either.
But . . .

A penguin can swim fast.
It uses its wings for swimming.

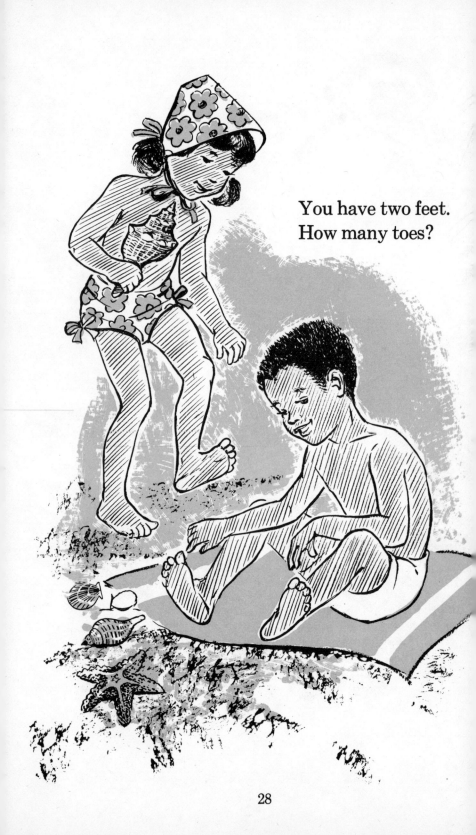

You have two feet.
How many toes?

This bird has two feet.
How many toes?

A bear has four feet.
Can you count its toes?

Does anything have four feet and only four toes?

A horse has four feet.
Each foot has one toe, and the
hoof is a toenail —

A supercolossal toenail!

You have a nose for smelling.
So does a rabbit.

What can smell without a nose?

A snail has no nose. It smells with two feelers on its head.

A lobster has no nose. It smells with
many little hairs on its body.
A lobster has two eyes for seeing.
Do you?

A puppy has two eyes.
A kitten has two eyes.

Does anything have eight eyes?
This kind of spider does.

WOLF SPIDER

You have teeth for chewing.
How many teeth do you have?

An elephant has teeth for chewing.
It can chew grass and leaves and sticks.
Can you guess how many chewing teeth it has?

An elephant has only four chewing teeth.
But they are very big and strong.

What can eat with no teeth at all?

Babies!